WELLINGTON S

The dragon kite

TESSA KRAILING

ILLUSTRATED BY
JON DAVIS

Nelson

The new words in this story are listed in the
appropriate Word Wall Worksheet in the Teacher's
Resource Pack for Level 4.

Thomas Nelson and Sons Ltd
Nelson House Mayfield Road
Walton-on-Thames Surrey
KT12 5PL UK

58 Albany Street
Edinburgh
EH1 3QR UK

Nelson Blackie
Wester Cleddens Road
Bishopbriggs
Glasgow
G64 2N2 UK

Thomas Nelson (Hong Kong) Ltd
Toppan Building 10/F
22a Westlands Road
Quarry Bay Hong Kong

Thomas Nelson Australia
102 Dodds Street
South Melbourne
Victoria 3205 Australia

Nelson Canada
1120 Birchmount Road
Scarborough Ontario
M1K 5G4 Canada

Text © Tessa Krailing 1989
Illustrations © Thomas Nelson and Sons Ltd 1992
Illustrated by Jon Davis

First published by Macmillan Education Ltd 1989

This edition published by Thomas Nelson and Sons Ltd 1992

ISBN 0-17-422734-5
NPN 9 8 7 6 5

Printed in Spain

Contents

Chow Wing Chan

Number 10 Wellington Square had been empty
for some time.
Before it was empty it had been a fish and
chip shop.
Now there was a SOLD sign outside.
Someone was moving in.
Number 10 was a shop with a flat over the top.
Rocky and Ben looked at the sign.
'The people who are moving in are called
Chow,' said Rocky.
'My Mum told me that they're Chinese.'
'Are they going to open a shop?' asked Ben.
'Yes,' said Rocky.
'A Chinese take-away.'
'That's good,' said Ben.
'I like Chinese food.
Lots of noodles and bean sprouts.'

The new boy from the Chinese take-away
was in school on Monday.
'This is Chow Wing Chan,' said Mr Belter.
'He comes from Hong Kong.
He can sit next to Jamila and you must
all help him to find his way around.'
Jamila smiled at the boy as he
sat down next to her.

'Hello, Chow,' she said.

'Chow is my family name,' said the boy.

'I'm called Wing Chan.'

'Oh,' said Jamila.

Jamila thought he looked unhappy.

'He must find it strange living in
Wellington Square after living in Hong Kong,'
she thought.

'We must try and make him feel at home.'

Later Jamila talked to Rocky and
Ben about Wing Chan.
'I think he's unhappy,' she said.
'We must try to make him feel at home.'
'Hey, Wing Chan,' called Rocky.
'Want to play football?'
Wing Chan didn't say anything.
He kept by himself and did not play
football with the others.
'He's not very friendly,' said Ben.
But Rocky could remember his first day.
He could remember what it was like to be new.

Chopsticks

When Rocky got home he told his Mum
about Wing Chan.
'I think he's unhappy,' said Rocky.
'I think he's missing his home in
Hong Kong.'
Rocky went to watch TV.
Ten minutes later his Mum came in.
'I've been thinking about Wing Chan,'
she said.
'Why don't you ask him to tea?
You can ask the other kids too.'

Next day, Rocky looked for Wing Chan.
He had asked Jamila, Ben, Tessa and
Tony to come to tea.
Now he was going to ask Wing Chan.
Wing Chan smiled.
'Yes, please,' he said.
'I should like that.'
'Great,' said Rocky.
'We'll go to my house after school.'

Rocky and Ben went home from school together.
'What are we going to have to eat?'
asked Ben.
'Don't know,' said Rocky.
'Mum never said.'
'Well,' said Ben, 'Chinese people don't
eat the same food as us.'
'What do they eat?' asked Rocky.
'Noodles, bean sprouts and lots of rice.'
'I don't think Mum is doing stuff like that,'
said Rocky.
They stopped outside Rocky's house.
'How do you know so much about Chinese
people?' asked Rocky.
'We've got a book at home,' said Ben.
'It says that Chinese people eat with
chopsticks.'
'Chopsticks?' said Rocky.
'Where are we going to get chopsticks from?'
'We've got chopsticks at home,' said Ben.
'I'll bring them tomorrow.'

The next day, after school, the children
went to Rocky's house.
Rocky's Mum smiled at Wing Chan.
'Hello, Wing Chan,' she said.
'I'm pleased you could come to tea.'
Wing Chan smiled but he didn't say anything.
'Come and sit down,' she said.
When they were all at the table, Rocky's
Mum brought in jelly and ice-cream.
'My favourite,' said Ben.
He got out his chopsticks and tried to
pick up the jelly with them.
The jelly fell on the table.
Soon there was jelly all over.
Everyone was laughing.
Everyone but Wing Chan.

13

Suddenly Wing Chan got up and
ran out of the room.
Everyone stopped laughing.
'Oh dear,' said Rocky's Mum.
'Wing Chan thinks you are making fun of
how Chinese people eat.'
'I wasn't,' said Ben.
'I was only trying to make him feel
at home.'
'We know that,' said Rocky's Mum.
'But you will have to tell Wing Chan.'
'He won't talk to us now,' said Rocky.
'He won't want to be friends.'

The dragon kite

Next day Rocky saw Wing Chan in the park.
Wing Chan had a big kite.
Rocky had seen kites before but
not like that.
'I've never seen a kite like that before,'
Rocky said.
Wing Chan told him that it was a
dragon kite.
Rocky watched Wing Chan as he flew the kite.
Would Wing Chan let him have a go?

The kite looked like a dragon.
It was very long.
It had lots of feathers on it.
Rocky thought it moved like a caterpillar.
'That's brilliant,' said Rocky.
'I've never seen such a brilliant kite.'

Ben came into the park.
They watched Wing Chan as he flew his kite.
Ben thought it was brilliant too.
'I would like a kite with feathers just
like that,' he said.
'So would I,' said Rocky.

The kite flew near some trees in the park.
Suddenly it dropped into the trees and
got stuck.
'It's stuck,' said Wing Chan.
'My kite has got stuck in the trees!'
Rocky ran over to him.
'I'll get it down,' he said.
'I'll climb the tree and get it down.'
Wing Chan looked at the tree.
'It's very big,' he said.
'You might fall.'
'I'll be careful,' said Rocky as he began to
climb up the tree.
'This way, Wing Chan will see that we want
to be friends with him,' he thought.

Rocky was half way up the tree when
Fred saw him.
'Hey!' shouted Fred.
'What do you think you're doing?
Get down from there!
No tree-climbing in my park!'
Rocky could hear Fred but he didn't
stop climbing.

The kite was stuck at the top of the tree.
Rocky had never climbed so far before.
But he had said he would get the kite so
he kept on climbing.
Wing Chan and Fred watched Rocky as
he went up the tree.
'What does he think he's doing?' said Fred.
'He shouldn't be up that tree.
He might fall.'
'He's going to get my kite,' said Wing Chan.
'It's stuck at the top of that tree.'
'Well, he's very silly,' said Fred crossly and
he shouted again.
'Come down, Rocky!
You might fall!'
But Rocky didn't come down.
He had nearly reached the kite.

Rocky could see the kite.
It was stuck on one of the top branches.
He crawled along the branch.
Rocky reached the end of the branch and
grabbed the kite.
'Got it!' he shouted.
Then he looked down.
He saw how far he had climbed.

Suddenly Rocky was scared.
He was a long way up.
He had climbed up the big tree and
got the kite but he couldn't climb down.
'I'm stuck,' he shouted.
Fred and Wing Chan didn't know what to do.
'Don't move!' shouted Fred.
'I'll get help!'

Friends

Just then WPC Clark came into the park.
'What's Rocky doing?' she asked.
'My kite got stuck in the top of that
big tree,' said Wing Chan.
'Yes,' said Fred.
'And the silly boy climbed up to get it back.
Now he's stuck in the tree.'
'We must get a long ladder,' said WPC Clark.
'Have you got one, Fred?'
'Yes,' said Fred.
'I'll go and get it.'
'Be quick,' said the policewoman.
'We've got to get Rocky down.'
Fred came back quickly with a long ladder.
WPC Clark took the ladder over to the tree.
'Don't move!' she called to Rocky.
'I'll be with you in a minute.
I'll get you down!'
WPC Clark climbed up the ladder.

Very soon she reached Rocky and
took the kite from him.
She got him onto the ladder and
they climbed down carefully.
'It was higher than I thought,' said Rocky.
'Well, don't do it again,' said
the policewoman.
'It was a very silly thing to do just
for a kite.'

'It's not just any kite,' said Wing Chan.
'It comes all the way from Hong Kong.'
Wing Chan was very pleased to have his
kite back.
'Would you like a go with my kite?'
he asked Rocky.
'Yes, please,' said Rocky.
He took the kite, and Fred and WPC Clark
watched him as he flew it.
'It's great!' said Rocky.
'Yes,' said WPC Clark.
'But be careful you don't get it stuck
in the tree again!'

Rocky and Wing Chan went home together.
They saw the others outside Mr Patel's shop.
Wing Chan called them over.
'My Dad is opening the shop today.
You can all come and eat with me.
I'll show you how to eat with chopsticks.
You eat noodles and bean sprouts and
rice with chopsticks, not jelly!'
They all laughed and Wing Chan did too.

29

'This is how you use chopsticks,'
said Mr Chow.
He picked up some noodles with
the chopsticks.
Rocky picked up some bean sprouts but
some of them fell on the table.

Ben had a go and so did the others.
Everyone laughed.
'I'm glad we came,' said Wing Chan.
'I'm glad we came to Wellington Square.'
'We're glad you came too,' said Tessa.
'Now we can eat Chinese food every day!'

After tea, Wing Chan brought out his kite.
He told the others how Rocky had got it
down from the big tree in the park.
'I made this kite,' said Wing Chan.
'Can you show us how to make one?'
asked Tony.
'Yes,' said Wing Chan.
'Then we will all have dragon kites.'
Wing Chan showed them how to make
a dragon kite.
Now there are lots of kites
in the park in Wellington Square.